GRADE

3

Daily Mathematics

CRITICAL THINKING
AND PROBLEM SOLVING

Great Source Education Group

A Houghton Mifflin Company
Wilmington, Massachusetts

Printed in the United States of America
International Standard Book Number: 0-8123-7596-3

6 7 8 9 10 - BP - 99 98 97 96

URL address: http://www.greatsource.com/

INTRODUCTION

Philosophy

DAILY MATHEMATICS is based on the principle that all students should have the opportunity to think mathematically every day. Therefore, the problems on these pages emphasize higher order thinking skills, not drill and practice.

Our goal is for students to discover, through the use of *DAILY MATHEMATICS*, that there is more than one way to approach a problem, and that frequently there is more than one correct answer. We hope that students will be rewarded for creativity in their approach to the process of solving problems and that the importance of merely finding "the answer" will be de-emphasized. While doing these problems, of course, students will get plenty of opportunity to practice their arithmetic skills—not only pencil-and - paper skills, but also estimation, mental mathematics, and calculator skills.

We believe that the richness of a student's mathematical experience is enhanced if arithmetic is taught not in isolation and devoid of application, but rather in conjunction with other branches of mathematics and in real-life situations. Therefore, *DAILY MATHEMATICS* helps students see connections among various topics— geometry, logic, probability, consumer applications, algebra, number sense, and data analysis—so that the situation is real and, therefore, interesting for students.

Finally, to encourage critical thinking among students, we would like the teacher to be supportive, not prescriptive. For example, on certain problems, one student might use paper and pencil, another the calculator, and still another, mental mathematics. Instead of considering one approach "right" and the other "wrong," you might discuss with the students why they chose the method they used. Similarly, in problems requiring estimation, consider accepting a wide range of answers as "reasonable"; the process is just as important as the result.

Time Management

The problems are designed for 5-10 minutes per day. Due to the richness of some of the problems, as well as the optional follow-up questions provided in some of the teacher's notes, discussion can occasionally proceed well beyond 10 minutes, if you allow it. Some teachers, therefore, might choose to use the program less often than daily and set aside more time, thus reducing the pressure to cut off discussion.

How to use *Daily Mathematics*

The program was designed to be used in a variety of ways to suit the preference of the individual teacher. Any of the following approaches, or any combination of them, is workable. The teacher can:
1. Write the problem on the chalkboard (to facilitate this approach, complicated art has been avoided);
   or
2. Photocopy the page, cut the problem out, and distribute it to each student;
   or
3. Make overhead transparencies;
   or
4. Dictate the problem to the students, while putting on the chalkboard any figure or data that is necessary.

The Teacher's Notes

Notes to the teacher are provided alongside every problem for easy reference. The notes include the following:
- The answer, when there is one correct answer
- Some sample answers when a variety of answers is possible
- Background notes containing useful mathematical or pedagogical information related to the problem
- Occasionally, a related follow-up question to ask students

DAILY MATHEMATICS STRANDS

Students using DAILY MATHE-MATICS are exposed to several important mathematics strands in addition to basic arithmetic skills. These strands, and the frequency with which they appear, are shown in the chart.

STRAND	1	2	3	4	5	6	7	8	9	10	11	12	13	14	15	16	17	18	19	20	21	22	23	24	25	26	27	28	29	30	31	32	33	34	35	36
Critical Thinking	●	●	●	●	●	●	●	●	●	●	●	●	●	●	●	●	●	●	●	●	●	●	●	●	●	●	●	●	●	●	●	●	●	●	●	●
Problem Solving	●	●	●	●	●	●	●	●	●	●	●	●	●	●	●	●	●	●	●	●	●	●	●	●	●	●	●	●	●	●	●	●	●	●	●	●
Geometry	●	●	●	●	●	●	●		●	●			●		●		●		●		●		●		●		●		●		●	●		●	●	●
Measurement	●	●		●		●	●		●		●	●	●	●	●	●	●	●	●	●	●	●	●	●	●	●	●	●								●
Estimation/ Mental Math	●	●	●	●	●	●	●	●	●	●	●	●	●	●	●	●	●	●	●	●	●	●	●	●	●	●	●	●	●	●	●	●		●	●	●
Logic	●	●	●	●	●	●	●	●	●	●	●	●	●	●	●	●	●	●	●	●	●	●	●	●	●	●	●	●	●	●	●	●	●	●	●	●
Probability/ Statistics		●		●	●		●	●		●	●		●		●		●				●	●		●		●	●		●			●				●
Patterns			●	●	●					●	●		●		●		●		●			●	●		●			●			●				●	
Number Sense	●	●	●	●	●	●	●	●	●	●	●	●	●	●	●	●	●	●	●	●	●	●	●	●	●	●	●	●	●	●	●	●	●	●	●	●
Consumer Applications	●	●		●		●	●		●			●	●	●	●	●	●			●	●			●	●			●	●		●			●		
Algebra		●		●					●			●			●		●							●			●	●								
Communicating Mathematics		●		●	●	●	●		●		●	●			●		●	●		●	●	●		●	●		●		●	●	●			●	●	●

Daily Mathematics / Week 1

1

6 routes

You may want to point out that the arrows indicate direction of travel.

Different routes: *ABF, ACF, ADEF, ADCF, ADCEF, ACEF*

DAY 1

Find the number of different routes from *A* to *F*.

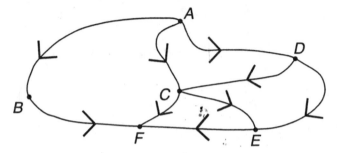

2

2 quarters

You may want to discuss with students how they solved the problem. Some students may take this approach: 71¢ – 10¢ = 61¢; 61¢ – 5¢ = 56¢; 56¢ – 6¢ = 50¢.

Others may do this: 10¢ + 5¢ + 6¢ = 21¢; 71¢ – 21¢ = 50¢.

It is important to stress that there is more than one approach to solving a problem. Some students may need to be reminded that a quarter is equal to 25¢.

DAY 2

Sam has 71¢. He has 1 dime, 1 nickel, and 6 pennies. The rest of his money is quarters. How many quarters does Sam have?

3

1. 1 yd, 25 in., 2 ft

2. 1 m, 2 dm, 3 cm

Some students may think that 25 in. is longer than 1 yd because 25 is greater than 1. You may wish to review the following:

    12 in. = 1 ft
     3 ft = 1 yd
    10 cm = 1 dm
    10 dm = 1 m

DAY 3

Order the lengths, from greatest to least.

1. 2 ft   1 yd   25 in.

2. 3 cm   1 m   2 dm

Daily Mathematics / Week 1

DAY 4

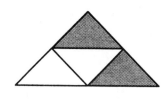 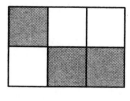 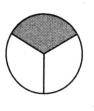

A   B   C

1. How many equal parts are there in each figure?

2. How many equal parts of each figure are shaded?

3. Write the fraction that tells what part of each figure is shaded.

4

1. Figure A: 4 equal parts; Figure B: 6 equal parts; Figure C: 3 equal parts

2. Figure A: 2 of the 4 parts; Figure B: 3 of the 6 parts; Figure C: 1 of the 3 parts

3. Figure A: $\frac{2}{4}$, or $\frac{1}{2}$; Figure B: $\frac{3}{6}$, or $\frac{1}{2}$; Figure C: $\frac{1}{3}$

You may want to extend this problem by asking students to divide Figure A into eighths, Figure B into twelfths, and Figure C into sixths. Then, have students answer the same three questions, and compare these answers to the original. This provides a good review of equivalent fractions.

DAY 5

Copy the diagram. The dots are 1 unit apart.

Connect the dots to make a shape that is 8 units around.

. . . . . .
. . . . . .
. . . . . .
. . . . . .
. . . . . .
. . . . . .

5

Answers will vary. Possible answers: 2 unit by 2 unit square; 1 unit by 3 unit rectangle

You might point out that the distance around (perimeter of) 2 different figures can be the same, even though the lengths and widths of the figures are different.

Teacher's Notes

1

Change the digital clock to show 5:10, or reverse the position of the hands on the analog clock so that the time is 2:25.

You may want to have students write similar questions to share with the class. These questions will provide practice for students that need help interpreting an analog clock.

2

1. 8 or 9 years old

2. 8 years old

The answer to problem 1 varies, depending on when Shirley's birthday is.

From the information given in problem 2, students should conclude that her birthday was 5 months ago. You may wish to use a calendar to demonstrate.

3

1. 49   2. 314   3. 197

These problems provide good practice on rounding. You can extend this problem by asking students to make the least 4-digit number possible using the given numbers. Then ask what this number is close to. (1,347; 1,000 to the nearest thousand or 1,300 to the nearest hundred) Do the same for the greatest 4-digit number. (9,743; 10,000 to the nearest thousand or 9,700 to the nearest hundred)

DAY 1

A digital clock shows

An analog clock shows

How could you make both clocks show the same time?

DAY 2

Shirley is 9 years old.

1. How old was she 6 months ago?

2. Suppose her birthday is 7 months from now. How old was she 6 months ago?

DAY 3

Use these digits only once.   1   9   4   7   3

1. Make a 2-digit number as close as possible to 50.

2. Make a 3-digit number as close as possible to 300.

3. Make a 3-digit number as close as possible to 200.

Daily Mathematics / Week 2

DAY 4

1. Suppose that you are facing east. If you turn left two times, then turn right three times, in what direction are you now facing?

2. From the direction you are now facing, turn right once, then turn left twice. What direction is behind you?

1. South

2. West

Explain to students that a *turn* is a 90° turn. It may be necessary to draw a basic N, S, E, W, directional finder on the chalkboard.

Problem 2 is an extension of problem 1. From directions in problem 2, you would be facing east, so west is behind you.

DAY 5

Which two figures are the same? Why?

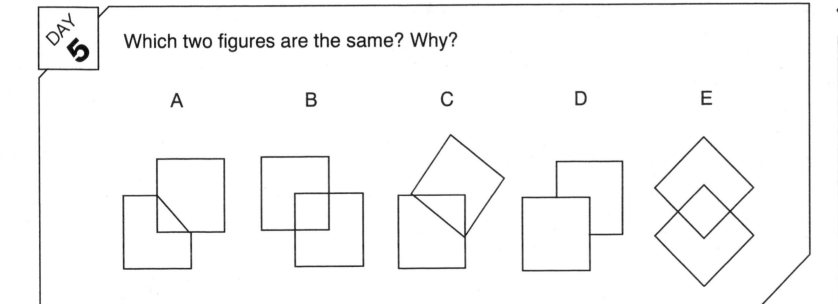

A   B   C   D   E

Figures B and E; Figures B and E are the same because one of the two figures can be turned and moved, or slid, so that if fits exactly on top of the other.

Teacher's Notes

1

40 squares

You may want to ask students how they solved the problem. The expression (8 × 8) − (12 × 2) may describe the process used by some students.

2

Susan: blue; Jean: yellow; Clare: green

A chart may help students organize their thinking.

	Blue	Yellow	Green
Susan	yes	no	no
Jean	no	yes	no
Clare	no	no	yes

Susan did not wear the yellow or green ribbon.

Jean did not wear the green ribbon and cannot wear the blue.

Clare cannot wear the blue or yellow ribbon.

3

1. 6   2. 25

You can ask students to explain the strategy they used to solve each problem. In problem 1, some students may have subtracted the sum of 7 and 19 from 32. In problem 2, some students may have subtracted 18 from 43.

DAY 1

A checkerboard has 8 squares on each side. Each player starts with 12 checkers on the board. How many squares do not have checkers on them at the start of the game?

DAY 2

There is a blue ribbon, a yellow ribbon, and a green ribbon. Susan did not wear the yellow ribbon or the green ribbon. Jean did not wear the green ribbon. Clare wore either the blue ribbon or the green ribbon.

What color ribbon did each girl wear?

DAY 3

Find the missing numbers.

1.
```
    7
    ?
 + 19
 ____
   32
```

2.
```
   43
 − ?
 ____
   18
```

Daily Mathematics / Week 3

DAY 4

How many 3-digit numbers can you make with the digits 3, 7, and 4?
What are the numbers?

4

Answers will vary. Possible answers:
6 (if digits are not repeated): 374, 347, 734, 743, 473, 437;
27 (if digits are repeated): 333, 337, 334, 377, 344, 373, 343, 374, 347, 777, 743, 734, 733, 744, 737, 747, 773, 774, 444, 443, 447, 474, 434, 473, 437, 433, 477

You may want to discuss with students how the question can be rewritten to be more specific. For example, "if each digit is used only once in each number" or "if each digit can be used more than once in each number" can be added at the end of the question.

DAY 5

In the square, the sum of the numbers in each row and column is 19.

Find the missing numbers.

9		4	19
	3	8	19
	10		19
19	19	19	

5

9	6	4	19
8	3	8	19
2	10	7	19
19	19	19	

You may want students to share their strategies for filling in the square.

1.

1. Even number   2. Even number   3. Odd number

Examples will vary. Possible examples:

1. 4 + 2 = 6; 20 + 8 = 28; 40 + 10 = 50

2. 1 + 3 = 4; 21 + 7 = 28; 39 + 11 = 50

3. 2 + 5 = 7; 12 + 9 = 21; 28 + 17 = 45

You may want to have students share their examples with the class.

2.

Ken, Mark, Jamie, Sam

You may want four students to act out the roles of Ken, Jamie, Sam, and Mark. Or, suggest that students make a list with the four names and rearrange the list of names until it matches the description.

3.

1. $1.33

2. Possible answers:
2 quarters, 1 dime, 1 nickel, and 2 pennies; 2 quarters, 3 nickels, and 2 pennies; 2 quarters, 1 dime, 7 pennies; 2 quarters, 2 nickels, 7 pennies; 1 quarter, 2 dimes, 4 nickels, 2 pennies; 1 quarter, 2 dimes, 3 nickels, 7 pennies; 1 quarter, 1 dime, 6 nickels, 2 pennies; 1 quarter, 1 dime, 5 nickels, 7 pennies; 1 quarter, 1 dime, 6 nickels, 2 pennies; 1 quarter, 1 dime, 5 nickels, 7 pennies

DAY 1

Is the sum an even number or an odd number?

1. even number + even number

2. odd number + odd number

3. even number + odd number

Write examples to check your answers.

DAY 2

Use this information to arrange the four boys in order of age, from oldest to youngest.

Jamie is older than Sam but younger than Ken. Mark is younger than Ken but older than Jamie.

DAY 3

You have 3 quarters, 2 dimes, 6 nickels, and 8 pennies.

1. How much money do you have?

2. Which coins could you use to make $0.67?

Daily Mathematics / Week 4

DAY 4

Find two numbers that add up to 15 and multiply out to 56.

4

7 and 8

You may want to rephrase the question as follows to familiarize students with the correct terminology: **Find two numbers whose sum is 15 and whose product is 56.** Suggest that students use a guess-and-check approach to solve this problem. A table may help students organize their thinking.

Addends of 15	Product of addends	
1 + 14 = 15	1 × 14 = 14	no
2 + 13 = 15	2 × 13 = 26	no
3 + 12 = 15	3 × 12 = 36	no
4 + 11 = 15	4 × 11 = 44	no
5 + 10 = 15	5 × 10 = 50	no
6 + 9 = 15	6 × 9 = 54	no
7 + 8 = 15	7 × 8 = 56	yes

DAY 5

1. Graph the points on the grid.

   a. Up 2, across 1

   b. Up 4, across 3

   c. Across 5, up 2

2. Connect the points.
What figure did you make?

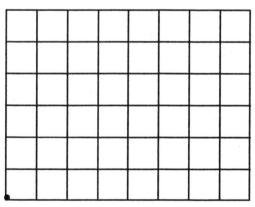

Start

5

1.

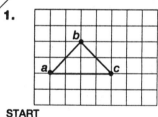

START

2. Triangle

Have students use grid paper or sketch the grid on paper. Remind students to begin at "Start" each time they graph a different point.

Teacher's Notes

1

1. 36
2. 64
3. #7

Students should see that if #6 = 36, #8 = 64, and #9 = 81, then #7 is the most likely answer.

These problems preview the concept of squaring a number (multiplying a number by itself).

2

1. They are all multiples of 7.
2. Possible answers: 14, 21, 42, 63, 70, 91, 98

3

56 legs (assuming all the animals have a normal number of limbs)

Students should know that fish do not have legs.

 DAY 1

Look at these problems:

#2 = 4   #5 = 25   #9 = 81

1. What number do you think is equal to #6?
2. What number do you think is equal to #8?
3. What do you think is equal to 49?

 DAY 2

1. What do these 2-digit numbers have in common?

56   84   35

77   49   28

2. Name other 2-digit numbers that have the same thing in common as these numbers.

DAY 3

Willie went to a pet store and saw 3 puppies, 5 cats, 30 fish, and 12 birds. How many legs do these animals have all together?

Daily Mathematics / Week 5

after 2-28

DAY 4

Jeff has three shirts and three pairs of pants.

How many different outfits can he make by mixing and matching his clothes?

4

9 outfits

Students may find a tree diagram helpful.

In the diagram, *S* will represent shirts and *P* will represent pants.

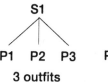

S1	S2	S3
P1 P2 P3	P1 P2 P3	P1 P2 P3
3 outfits	3 outfits	3 outfits

$3 + 3 + 3 = 9$, or $3 \times 3 = 9$

DAY 5

How many faces does each figure have?

1.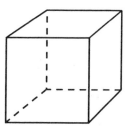

2.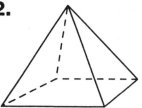

5

1. 6 faces   **2.** 5 faces

Students may have difficulty recognizing these figures as three dimensional. You may want to bring actual objects to class that are shaped like a cube or a pyramid. Remind students to include the bottom faces.

Teacher's Notes

1

24 pictures

You may need to remind students that each box has 6 faces. So, Sylvia will need 6 pictures per box.

6 + 6 + 6 + 6 = 24, or 6 × 4 = 24

2

1. 18 quarters

2. 45 dimes

You may want to have various students share with the class the different approaches they used to solve the problems.

3

Answers will vary. Possible answers: Both are 4-sided figures. Both have 4 right angles. A square has all sides equal and a rectangle has opposite sides equal.

DAY 1

Sylvia is decorating a box. She puts a picture of a different flower on each side of the box. If Sylvia wants to decorate 4 boxes, how many pictures of flowers will she need?

DAY 2

Henry has $4.50.

1. If all the money were in quarters, how many quarters would he have?

2. If all the money were in dimes, how many dimes would he have?

DAY 3

Draw a square and a rectangle. How are they alike?

How are they different?

1. How many students in Mr. Bell's class have blue eyes?

2. What eye color do most students in Mr. Bell's class have?

3. How many more students in Mr. Bell's class have blue eyes than green eyes?

4. How many students are in Mr. Bell's class?

EYE COLOR OF 3RD GRADERS IN MR. BELL'S CLASS

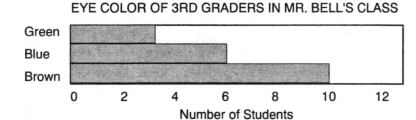

I am a number between 20 and 26.
I am a multiple of 3.
I am an odd number.

What number am I?

1. 6 students

2. Brown

3. 3 students

4. 19 students

You may want to extend this problem by having your class construct a bar graph about a topic of their choice that would include all the students. For example, hair color of students, types of instruments played by students, type of pets students have, etc.

21

If students answer 24, explain that 24 is a multiple of 3, but it is an even number.

Teacher's Notes

1

1:11, 2:22, 3:33, 4:44, 5:55, and 11:11

DAY 1

At what times are all the digits shown by a digital clock the same?

2

Any straight line that passes through the central dot (dot in 2nd row and 2nd column) without passing through any of the others is a possible solution.

DAY 2

How can you draw a straight line so that there are 4 dots on each side of the line?

• • •

• • •

• • •

3

475

The ones digit must be 5 (odd number), the tens digit is 5 + 2 = 7, and the hundreds digit is 7 – 3 = 4.

DAY 3

I am a 3-digit number.
My ones digit is a 4 or a 5.
My tens digit is 2 greater than my ones digit.
My hundreds digit is 3 fewer than my tens digit.
I am an odd number.

What number am I?

Daily Mathematics / Week 7

The Calico train makes 5 stops between Huntsville and Calico. There are 15 miles between each stop. The Mayville train makes 4 stops between Sunnydale and Mayville. There are 20 miles between each stop.

Which train travels the greater number of miles?

The Mayville train

The Mayville train travels $4 \times 20 = 80$ miles. The Calico train travels $5 \times 15 = 75$ miles.

In which figures is $\frac{1}{3}$ shaded?

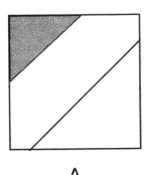

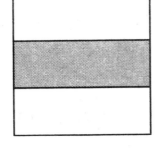

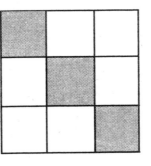

A   B   C

Figures B and C

You may need to remind students that *thirds* imply one of three equal parts. Since Figure A is not divided into equal parts, the shaded region does not represent $\frac{1}{3}$ of the figure. Since $\frac{3}{9} = \frac{1}{3}$, $\frac{1}{3}$ of Figure C is shaded. You may want to have students copy Figure C and cut it into 9 parts. Suggest that students rearrange the shaded pieces vertically or horizontally to better see that $\frac{1}{3}$ of the figure is shaded. This type of activity may help the visual learner.

Teacher's Notes

1

Red; There are more red than black socks.

You may want to try a similar experiment with your class. This problem previews the concept of probability.

2

8,456

Students may solve this problem by working backward — multiplying the quotient by the divisor and adding the remainder. You may want to allow students to use a calculator to facilitate the number-crunching portion of the problem.

3

1. 123,456,789   2. 987,654,321

You may want students to practice saying these numbers aloud: one hundred twenty-three million, four hundred fifty-six thousand, seven hundred eighty-nine; nine hundred eighty-seven million, six hundred fifty-four thousand, three hundred twenty-one

DAY 1

There are 6 red socks and 2 black socks in a drawer. If you reach in and pull out one sock, what color do you think it will be? Why?

DAY 2

Find the dividend. Use your calculator.

$$21\overline{)????} \quad \underset{}{402} \text{ R14}$$

DAY 3

1. What is the least 9-digit number that can be made using all of the digits from 1 through 9?

2. What is the greatest 9-digit number that can be made using all of the digits from 1 through 9?

Daily Mathematics / Week 8

DAY 4

	Test 1	Test 2	Test 3
Jamie	B	B	A
Katie	A	B	D
Patrice	C	A	B

1. What grade did Katie get on the second test?

2. Who received a B on the third test?

3. If an A is worth 4 points, a B is worth 3 points, a C is worth 2 points, and a D is worth 1 point, who received the greatest number of points for all the tests?

4

1. B

2. Patrice

3. Jamie

This exercise gives students the opportunity to read and interpret data displayed in rows and columns.

DAY 5

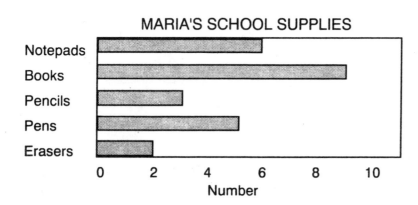

MARIA'S SCHOOL SUPPLIES

Notepads, Books, Pencils, Pens, Erasers

Number

1. How many pencils does Maria have?

2. How many more books does Maria have than pens?

3. How many notepads and erasers does Maria have in all?

5

1. 3 pencils

2. 4 more books

3. 8 notepads and erasers

Maria has 9 books and 5 pens, and 6 notepads and 2 erasers.

You might extend this exercise by asking students to draw a bar graph that represents their school supplies.

Daily Mathematics / Week 9

1

June 9, June 18, and June 27

The solution to this problem is based on the common multiples of 3 and 9 between 3 and 30.

DAY 1

In June, Marcus will play a tennis game every third day, beginning June 3. He will play a baseball game every ninth day, beginning June 9.

On what days in June will he play both a tennis game and a baseball game?

2

8,527

The 8 is in the thousands place, the 5 is in the hundreds place, the 2 is in the tens place, and the 7 is in the ones place.

This problem gives students practice identifying place value, and even and odd numbers.

DAY 2

Use the numbers 7, 2, 5, and 8.

Put the greater even number in the thousands place.
Put the lesser odd number in the hundreds place.
Put the lesser even number in the tens place.
Put the greater odd number in the ones place.

What is the number?

3

7 choices

You may want to sketch the 8 by 8 checkerboard, or bring the actual board to class. Each player starts with 12 checkers, 4 to a row. With the first move, they can move 3 of the checkers in 2 different ways, and 1 checker in 1 way.

DAY 3

Look at a checkerboard.

You are about to start a game of checkers with a friend. How many choices do you have for your first move?

DAY 4

The Cougars basketball team played two games against the Bobcats. In the games, the Cougars scored a total of 96 points, and the Bobcats scored a total of 89 points.

1. Write possible scores for both games showing the Cougars winning.

2. Write possible scores for both games showing the Cougars losing one game.

4

Answers will vary.

Possible answers:

1. Cougars: 48; Bobcats: 44
   Cougars: 48; Bobcats: 45

2. Cougars: 60; Bobcats: 40
   Cougars: 36; Bobcats: 49

DAY 5

The map shows some of the streets in a city.

Peter was on the corner of Second Avenue and C Street. He walked 1 block north, 1 block east, 3 blocks south, and 2 blocks west.

Where is he now?

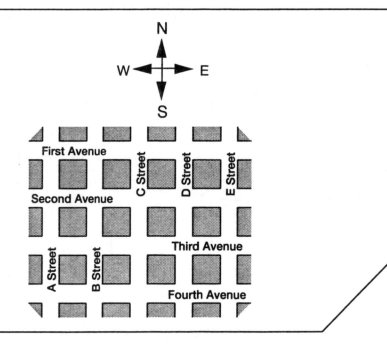

5

Corner of Fourth Avenue and B Street

You may wish to have the students write directions for Peter to go from where he is now to the corner of First Avenue and E Street by crossing Second Avenue and C Street.

Daily Mathematics / Week 10

1

Answers may vary. Possible answers:

1. 17 + 36 = 53, the sum closest to 50.

2. 17 + 36 + 97 = 150, totals exactly 150.

3. 97 + 66 + 89 = 252, the sum closest to 250.

Students may guess and check to find the answers. Calculators may be helpful. These exercises give students practice with rounding numbers.

DAY 1

Use these numbers.   17   89   66

97   74   36

Find groups of two or three numbers with sums closest to

1. 50   **2.** 150   **3.** 250

2

13 times

The number of Tuesdays in April is extra information.

DAY 2

The Science Club meets every Thursday after school. There were 4 Thursdays in February, 5 Thursdays in March, and 4 Thursdays in April. There were 4 Tuesdays in April.

How many times did the Science Club meet in the three months?

3

Sally and John

30 cm is equal to 3 dm. 3 m does not equal 30 cm. You may need to remind students that 1 m = 10 dm and 1 m = 100 cm. Or, students may use a metric ruler to help them solve this problem.

DAY 3

Sally found the perimeter of the rectangle to be 30 cm. John said the perimeter is equal to 3 dm and Carl said it is equal to 3 m. Who is correct?

10 cm

5 cm   5 cm

10 cm

Daily Mathematics / Week 10

DAY 4

An airline pilot flew 1,054 miles on Tuesday, 1,540 miles on Wednesday, and 450 fewer miles on Thursday than on Wednesday.

1. How many miles did the pilot fly on Thursday?

2. How many miles did the pilot fly all together in those three days?

3. On which day did the pilot fly the fewest number of miles?

1. 1,090 miles

2. 3,684 miles

3. Tuesday; 1,054 miles

DAY 5

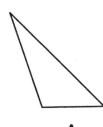 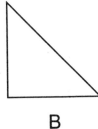 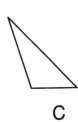 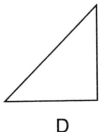

A   B   C   D

1. Which triangles have the same shape?

2. Which triangles have the same shape and size?

5

1. Triangles A and C; Triangles B and D

2. Triangles B and D

Triangles that are the same shape, but not the same size are called *similar* triangles.

Triangles that are the same shape and same size are called *congruent* triangles. All congruent triangles are similar, but not all similar triangles are congruent. You may want to point out that Triangle B (or Triangle D) can be turned and slid to fit on Triangle D (Triangle B).

Teacher's Notes

1

1. Juan
2. Mike

You may want to choose three students to act out the roles of Mike, Juan, and Sarah.

2

c. Possible answer:

ELECTION RESULTS

Number of Votes

400
300
200
100
0

Parks   Smith   Ferris
Candidates

You may want to discuss how a. and b. can be changed so that information can be represented as a bar graph.

3

1. 863
2. 1,346
3. 8,634
4. 14,683

These problems review the concept of even and odd numbers, and place value.

DAY 1

Mike lives farther away from school than Sarah. Juan lives closer to school than Sarah.

1. Who lives the closest to school?

2. Who lives the farthest away from school?

DAY 2

Choose the information that can be shown in a bar graph. Then make a sample bar graph for it.

a. Number of people who watched a movie on Wednesday

b. Number of Tuesdays in May

c. Number of votes received by three candidates in an election

DAY 3

Use these numbers.   8   1   4   3   6

1. Write the greatest 3-digit odd number.

2. Write the least 4-digit even number.

3. Write the greatest 4-digit even number.

4. Write the least 5-digit odd number.

Daily Mathematics / Week 11

DAY 4

The table shows the number of book reports written by the third and fourth grades during a three-month period.

1. In which month were the greatest number of book reports written?

2. Which grade wrote fewer book reports?

BOOK REPORTS WRITTEN		
Month	Grade 3	Grade 4
February	115	131
March	136	117
April	123	109

4

1. March

2. Grade 4

You may need to explain the difference between the rows and the columns of the table. To answer problem 1, students must add the rows of the table. To answer problem 2, students must add the columns.

DAY 5

Match.

Column 1

1. $(7 + 5) \times 2$

2. $(8 \times 2) + 1$

3. $3 + (3 \times 4)$

4. $5 + (0 + 15)$

Column 2

a. $(5 \times 0) + 15$

b. $(3 + 3 + 4) \times 2$

c. $7 + (5 \times 2)$

d. $(3 + 3) \times 4$

5

1. d   2. c   3. a   4. b

These problems preview order of operations. Stress to students that operations within parentheses must be done first. You may want to discuss how regrouping the numbers in Column 1, problem 1 and Column 2c, and Column 1, problem 3 and Column 2d changes the value of the expressions.

Teacher's Notes

1

10; 15

To find the triangular number after 6, add a row of four dots: 6 + 4 = 10. To find the next triangular number after 10, add a row of five dots: 10 + 5 = 15.

You may suggest that students continue the diagram pattern to help them answer the question. Or, you may want to extend the problem by asking students to find the 10th triangular number. (55)

The numbers 1, 3, and 6 are called *triangular numbers.*

1   3   6

What are the next two triangular numbers?

2

The total value of the coins is $1.80. Stan can give Greg one dime and one nickel so that they both have $0.90.

Greg has 2 quarters, 1 dime, and 3 nickels.
Stan has 3 quarters, 2 dimes, and 2 nickels.

How can they share the coins so that they both have the same amount of money?

3

Red marker or blue marker

You may ask students to try a similar experiment. Point out that the chances of pulling out the red or blue marker are equally likely. You can extend the problem by using 2 red markers and 1 blue marker. Then, the student is more likely to pull out a red marker simply because there are more red than blue markers.

Suppose you have one blue marker and one red marker in your desk. You reach for one of the markers without looking. Which marker do you think you will pull out?

Daily Mathematics / Week 12

DAY 4

In how many different ways can Leon, Jason, and Liz line up to buy tickets for a movie?

6 ways

You may want to suggest that students draw a tree diagram to help them solve this problem.

First	Second	Third	
Leon	Jason	Liz	1
	Liz	Jason	2
Jason	Leon	Liz	3
	Liz	Leon	4
Liz	Leon	Jason	5
	Jason	Leon	6

DAY 5

Try these problems on your calculator.

1. ☐ 0 ÷ ☐ 4 =
2. ☐ 4 ÷ ☐ 0 =
3. ☐ 0 ÷ ☐ 7 =
4. ☐ 7 ÷ ☐ 0 =

What conclusion can you draw?

1. 0 **2.** Error message **3.** 0 **4.** Error message
You cannot divide by zero.

Students have been taught that if 6 ÷ 3 = 2, then 3 × 2 = 6. Therefore, if 0 ÷ 4 = 0, then 4 × 0 = 0. But, if 4 ÷ 0 = 0, then it should be true that 0 × 0 = 4. Since 0 × 0 ≠ 4, stress that you cannot divide by 0.

Teacher's Notes

1

1. 99,100

2. The ones, the tens, and the hundreds places

To extend this problem, you may want to ask students what is the least whole number that could be added to 99,095 to change the digit in the thousands place. (905) Some students may use the guess-and-check approach. Others may realize that 100,000 − 99,095 = 905. Students may find a calculator helpful.

2

1981

Students may make the mistake of subtracting 5 from 1976 rather than adding.

3

5:14

You may want to ask students to identify the extra information in this problem. (Larry started to read at 4:42.)

DAY 1

1. What number is 5 greater than 99,095?

2. In what places did the digits change?

DAY 2

Saul was born in 1976. His brother is 5 years younger than he is.

In what year was his brother born?

DAY 3

Larry read his book for 34 minutes. He started at 4:42 P.M. Kathy read her book for 15 minutes more than Larry read his book. She started reading at 4:25 P.M.

What time did Kathy finish reading her book?

DAY 4

Beatrice is buying a paint set that costs $7.49. She wants to give the clerk the exact amount. What is the fewest number of bills and coins she can use to pay for the paint set?

4

3 bills and 7 coins; one $5 bill, two $1 bills, one quarter, two dimes, and four pennies

To extend this question, ask what is the fewest number of bills and coins Beatrice would receive in change if she paid for the paint set with a $10 bill. (2 bills and 3 coins: two $1 bills, 2 quarters, 1 penny) Suggest that students count up from $7.49 to $10.

DAY 5

Ben, Debbie, Cal, and Meg sit in the same row in their classroom. There are 4 desks in the row. Ben sits directly behind Meg. Debbie is not behind Cal. Meg sits in the first seat.

In what order do they sit in the row?

5

Meg, Ben, Debbie, and Cal

We know Meg is in the first seat and Ben sits behind Meg. Since Debbie does not sit behind Cal, she must sit behind Ben, and Cal must sit behind her.

1. Each number after the second number is the sum of the two numbers before it.

2. 13, 21, 34, 55, 89

The sequence of numbers in this problem is called a Fibonacci sequence.

1, 1, 2, 3, 5, 8

1. What is the pattern?

2. Write the next five numbers in the pattern.

$2

You may want to discuss with students the reason Vivian gave the clerk $10.17 instead of $10, since her bill was only $8.17. (The clerk was able to give her two $1 bills as change instead of a $1 bill, 3 quarters, 1 nickel, and 3 pennies.)

Vivian bought four items at the store costing $2.17, $1.68, $3.20, and $1.12. She gave the clerk $10.17. How much change did she get?

3:55 P.M.

The meeting ended at 4:15 P.M. and Carmen started her talk 20 minutes before that, or 3:55.

The club meeting started at 3:15 P.M. and lasted one hour. Carmen gave a 20-minute talk at the end of the meeting. What time did Carmen begin her talk?

Daily Mathematics / Week 14

DAY 4

The sum of the numbers in each row, each column, and along each diagonal is 33. Find the missing numbers.

33   33

8		10	33
	11	9	33
	7		33

33   33   33

4

33   33

| 8 | 15 | 10 | 33
|----|----|----|
| 13 | 11 | 9 | 33
| 12 | 7 | 14 | 33

33   33   33

You may want to ask students to share their strategies for solving the square.

DAY 5

Tanya jogs around the school yard. The yard measures 40 feet on each of four sides. It measures 50 feet on the remaining side.

1. What shape is the school yard?

2. How many feet does Tanya jog around the yard?

3. Does Tanya jog more than 80 yards?

5

1. Pentagon (The yard has five sides.)

2. 210 feet

3. No

You may want to discuss how students found the perimeter (distance around) of the school yard.

Possible ways:
40 ft + 40 ft + 40 ft + 40 ft + 50 ft = 210 ft;
(40 ft × 4) + 50 ft = 210 ft
Stress that there is more than one way to solve a problem. You may need to remind students that 3 ft = 1 yd.

Teacher's Notes

1

Tom will be 10 years old and Ray will be 9 years old.

Ray will not be 10 until March 16, 1992.

2

Answers will vary. Possible answers: Divided the number by 2; subtracted 12 from the number; took half of the number

Have students put other numbers into the machine and apply their rule. This problem previews the concept of functions.

3

Possible answer:

JESSICA'S EARNINGS

Bar graph with y-axis "Money Earned" labeled $0 to $6, x-axis "Days" with Mon., Tues., Wed. Bars: Mon. $4, Tues. $3.50, Wed. $5.

DAY 1

Ray's birthday is March 16. Tom's birthday is February 11. They were both born in 1982. How old will they each be on March 1, 1992?

DAY 2

You put the number 24 into the machine.
The number 12 comes out.
What did the machine do to the number?

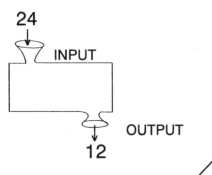

24

↓

INPUT

OUTPUT

12

DAY 3

Jessica earned $4 on Monday, $3.50 on Tuesday, and $5 on Wednesday.
Show this information on a bar graph.

DAY 4

Janet spent $0.92 less than Yanie on school supplies.
Gary spent $1.15 more than Janet.

1. Who spent the most on school supplies?

2. Who spent the least?

1. Gary

2. Janet

You may need to point out that if Gary spent $1.15 more than Janet, he spent more than Yanie. You can extend this problem by asking how much more Gary spent than Yanie. ($1.15 – $0.92 = $0.23)

DAY 5

Bob, Ted, Wilma, and Eva went hiking. They each hiked for 2 hours.
Bob hiked 5 miles every hour, Ted hiked 8 miles in 2 hours, Wilma hiked
3 miles every half hour, and Eva hiked 3 miles every hour.

1. How many miles did they each hike?

2. Who hiked the greatest number of miles?

3. Who hiked the fewest number of miles?

1. Bob: 10 miles; Ted: 8 miles; Wilma: 12 miles; Eva: 6 miles

2. Wilma

3. Eva

Bob: 5 miles per hour × 2 hours = 10 miles;
Wilma: 3 miles per half hour =
6 miles per hour × 2 hours = 12 miles;
Eva: 3 miles per hour × 2 hours = 6 miles

Teacher's Notes

Daily Mathematics / Week 16

1

8:08, 8:18, 8:28, 8:38, 8:48, and 8:58; 11:11

Remind students that a palindrome reads the same forward or backward, for example the number 222 or the word *mom*.

DAY 1

At what times does a digital clock show palindromes between 8 o'clock and 9 o'clock? Between 11 o'clock and 12 o'clock?

2

27

It is the only number between 10 and 30 that is an odd number whose digits (2 + 7) add up to 9. Suggest that students use the guess-and-check method to solve this problem.

DAY 2

Bernie is thinking of a number between 10 and 30. He says the number is an odd number and the sum of the digits is 9. What is the number?

3

1. Kareem

2. 20 minutes

Suggest that students solve the problem mentally. You may need to remind students that there are 60 minutes in one hour. Tina slept 8 hours × 60 minutes per hour, or 480, minutes. 500 minutes is longer than 480 minutes.

DAY 3

Last night Tina slept for 8 hours. Kareem slept for 500 minutes.

1. Who slept longer?

2. How much longer?

Daily Mathematics / Week 16

DAY 4

1. Which is closest to 10 liters?

10 pints   10 quarts   10 gallons

2. Which is closest to 28 meters?

28 inches   28 feet   28 yards

1. 10 quarts   **2.** 28 yards

You might want to bring the following units of measure to class: a pint, a quart, a gallon, and a liter container, and a meter stick and a yard stick. Then, the visual learner may be able to make better estimates.

DAY 5

Which two shapes are the same?

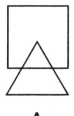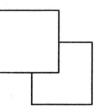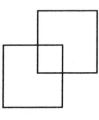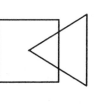

A   B   C   D   E

5

Figures A and E

Figure A (or Figure E) can be turned and slid to fit on Figure E (or Figure A). This problem previews the geometric concepts of rotation and translation.

1

1 quarter, 2 dimes, and 1 nickel

DAY 1

Martha has 4 coins. Their value is $0.50. What coins does she have?

2

100°C, 78°F, 50°F, 5°C

You may want to remind students that a Fahrenheit temperature is approximately 32° more than twice the Celsius temperature. Suggest that students estimate to solve this problem.

DAY 2

Write these temperatures in order, from greatest to least:

5°C, 50°F, 78°F, 100°C

3

Andrea: June; Matilda: April; Steve: October

You may want to provide a calendar for the visual learner.

DAY 3

Andrea's birthday is in the sixth month of the year.
Matilda's birthday is two months before Andrea's.
Steve's birthday is six months after Matilda's.

In what months were each of them born?

Daily Mathematics / Week 17

DAY 4

Match the fraction in Column 1 to an equivalent fraction in Column 2.

Column 1   Column 2

1. $\dfrac{2}{6}$ a. $\dfrac{2}{8}$

2. $\dfrac{1}{4}$ b. $\dfrac{2}{3}$

3. $\dfrac{1}{2}$ c. $\dfrac{1}{3}$

4. $\dfrac{4}{6}$ d. $\dfrac{3}{6}$

4

1. c   **2.** a   **3.** d   **4.** b

You may want to provide diagrams for the visual learner.

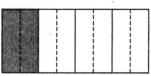

$\frac{1}{3} = \frac{2}{6}$ $\frac{1}{4} = \frac{2}{8}$

$\frac{1}{2} = \frac{3}{6}$ $\frac{2}{3} = \frac{4}{6}$

DAY 5

1. Which letters are in the circle?

2. Which letters are in the square and the circle?

3. Which letters are in the circle or the square?

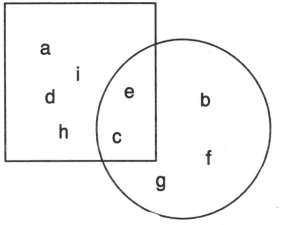

5

1. b, c, e, f, g

2. c and e

3. a, b, c, d, e, f, g, h, i

You may want to point out that "c" and "e" are in the circle, in the square, and in both the circle *and* the square (the intersection). All of the letters are in either the circle *or* the square (the union).

Teacher's Notes

1.
1. No
2. Possible answer: A baseball would have more mass than a balloon.

You may need to remind students that the mass of an object refers to a quantity of matter and the weight of an object refers to the pull of gravity.

2.
September

There are 9 letters in the name September and it is the ninth month of the year. This problem provides students with a chance to review the spelling of the twelve months.

3.
Craig, Peg, and Sal

Craig finished the race ahead of Peg, and Peg finished before Sal. You may want to have three students act out this problem.

DAY 1

1. Does a smaller object always have less mass than a larger object?

2. Give an example to explain your answer.

DAY 2

What month has the same number of letters in its name as the number of the month it is in the calendar year?

DAY 3

Sal, Peg, and Craig ran in a 100-meter race. Peg finished the race ahead of Sal. Craig finished the race before Peg.

In what order did they finish the race?

DAY 4

The dots in the diagram are 1 unit apart.

1. What is the perimeter of the figure?

2. What are the dimensions of a square with the same perimeter?

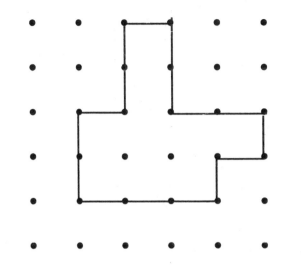

DAY 5

On Marla's fourth birthday, her Uncle Harry gave her $3. Every fourth year he gives her twice the previous amount. How much will Uncle Harry give Marla on her twelfth birthday?

Teacher's Notes

1

1. 10 out of 10, or 100%

2. No chance, or 0%

The only color marble that can be taken from the sack is a yellow marble.

2

1. 10 groups

2. 20 groups

You may want to point out that since 3 is half of 6, there are twice as many 3-minute groups in one hour as there are 6-minute groups.

3

$6 \times 4 = 24$; $6 \times 6 = 36$

You may need to point out to students that although 36 has many factors, the square must be replaced by the same number. So, the square is equal to 6 because $6 \times 6 = 36$. Then, since we are looking for the numbers that make both statements true at the same time, the square is equal to 6 in the first statement also.

DAY 1

Tim has a sack with 10 yellow marbles. He pulls one marble out of the sack.

1. What is the chance that the marble he pulled from the sack is yellow?

2. What is the chance that the marble is red?

DAY 2

There are 6 groups of 10 minutes in one hour.

1. How many groups of 6 minutes are there in one hour?

2. How many groups of 3 minutes are there?

DAY 3

Replace ☐ and △ with numbers that make both statements true at the same time.

☐ X △ = 24

☐ X ☐ = 36

DAY 4

You have a spinner labeled 1, 2, 3, 4, and 5 and you spin the arrow 5 times. You record the numbers you spin and add them.

1. What is the least sum you could have?

2. What is the greatest sum you could have?

1. 5   **2.** 25

If you spin 1 (the least number on the spinner) each time you will have 1 + 1 + 1 + 1 + 1 = 5; if you spin 5 (the greatest number on the spinner) each time you will have 5 + 5 + 5 + 5 + 5 = 25.

DAY 5

You want to buy a package of stickers for $0.89 and a paint brush for $0.39. You have $1.50. Can you buy these items?

Yes

Encourage students to use mental calculations to solve this problem. Point out that $0.89 is less than $1 and $0.39 is less than $0.50, so the cost of both items is less than $1.50.

Teacher's Notes

1

25 gallons

You may want to point out to students that it is very important to carefully read the problem. The question asks for the number of gallons of milk, not half gallons. There are 5 crates with 5 gallons (10 half gallons) in each crate and 5 gallons × 5 crates = 25 gallons.

2

23rd century

You may need to explain that 1-100 was the 1st century, 101-200 was the 2nd century, 201-300 was the 3rd century, and so on.

3

$\frac{3}{8}$ of his shirts

Angelo had a total of 8 shirts. He gave 3 of his 8 shirts to Dino.

DAY 1

A crate contains 10 cartons of milk. Each carton holds a half gallon of milk. There are 5 crates. How many gallons of milk are there in all?

DAY 2

What century will the year 2234 be in?

DAY 3

Angelo has 2 blue shirts, a green shirt, 3 white shirts, and 2 red shirts. He gave his brother, Dino, 3 of his shirts. What fraction of the shirts did Angelo give to Dino?

Daily Mathematics / Week 20

DAY 4

Look at these multiplication problems.

$$6 \times 7 = 42$$

$$6 \times 77 = 462$$

$$6 \times 777 = 4,662$$

1. Without multiplying, what do you think 6 x 7,777 is?

2. What is the pattern that you see?

4

1. 46,662

2. For each 7 that is added to the factor, a 6 is added between the 4 and the 2 of the product.

DAY 5

How could you shade the parts to show the fraction?

1. $\frac{6}{10}$

2. $\frac{5}{9}$

3. $\frac{4}{8}$

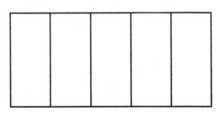

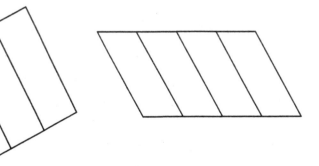

5

Possible answers:

1. $\frac{6}{10}$ 2. $\frac{5}{9}$ 3. $\frac{4}{8}$

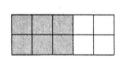
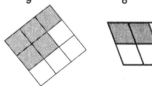

You may need to remind students that one half of fifths is tenths, one third of thirds is ninths, and one half of fourths is eighths.

Teacher's Notes

They will have the same number of pens.

Some students may need to use counters to see this. For example, give Lila 10 counters and Vic 6. This will help them see that if Lila gives 2 of her counters to Vic, they will both have 8 counters. The same will be true for any other pair of numbers where one number is four more than the other.

DAY 1

Lila has four more pens than Vic.
What happens when Lila gives Vic two of her pens?

No; Patrick would only have 6 cookies ($\frac{1}{2}$ dozen) left. You may need to remind students that 1 dozen = 12 and $\frac{1}{2}$ dozen = 6.

DAY 2

Patrick baked 3 dozen cookies. He sold $2\frac{1}{2}$ dozen of them at the fair.
Does Patrick have enough cookies left to give one to each of 12 friends? Explain.

1. 1 + 3 + 5 + 7 = 16
2. 9 book markers; 25 – 16 = 9

DAY 3

Lee Ann made 25 book markers for her friends. She gave 1 to Joseph, 3 to Richard, 5 to Carol, and 7 to Sandy.

1. Write a number sentence to show how many book markers Lee Ann gave to all of her friends.

2. How many book markers does she have left?

Daily Mathematics / Week 21

DAY 4

Use the target at the right.

red = 20 points

blue = 15 points

green = 10 points

yellow = 5 points

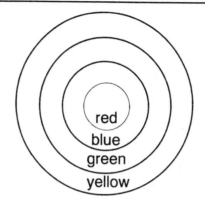

red
blue
green
yellow

Dick hit the red and green circles twice, and the yellow circle three times. Janice hit the red and the yellow circles once, the blue circle three times, and the green circle twice.

Who had the higher score?

4

Janice

Janice scored: 20 + 5 + (3 × 15) + (2 × 10) = 90 points.

Dick scored: (2 × 20) + (2 × 10) + (3 × 5) = 75 points.

DAY 5

Jason, Brian, Carla, and Lisa sold a total of 100 tickets. Jason sold $\frac{1}{8}$ of the tickets, Brian sold $\frac{1}{4}$ of the tickets, Carla sold $\frac{3}{8}$ of the tickets, and Lisa sold $\frac{1}{4}$ of the tickets.

1. Who sold the greatest number of tickets?

2. Who sold the fewest number of tickets?

3. Who sold one quarter of the tickets?

5

1. Carla

2. Jason

3. Brian and Lisa

$\frac{3}{8}$ is greater than $\frac{1}{4}$ and greater than $\frac{1}{8}$.

You may need to point out that it is not necessary to know the exact number of tickets sold by each person, but rather how to compare and order fractions.

Teacher's Notes

1

Fold the paper in half, fold it in half again, and fold it in half again.

2

12 inches

First find the perimeter of the four sides:
7 + 7 + 7 + 7 = 28, or 7 × 4 = 28. Then subtract the 28 inches from the 40 inches to get 12 inches.

3

$2\frac{1}{2}$ cups

Since 30 muffins is equal to $2\frac{1}{2}$ dozen muffins, Julia needs $2\frac{1}{2}$ cups of blueberries.

DAY 1

Take a piece of paper 8 inches long.

How could you mark the inches on the piece of paper without using a ruler?

DAY 2

The perimeter of a five-sided figure is 40 inches. Four of the sides measure 7 inches each. What is the length of the fifth side?

DAY 3

Julia's blueberry muffin recipe calls for a cup of blueberries for every dozen muffins. If Julia bakes 30 muffins, how many cups of blueberries will she need?

DAY 4

Nora and Dora wrote a 5-page story. Each page had about 125 words.
About how many words did the story have?

4

Answers will vary. About 625 words

Encourage students to estimate mentally.

$100 \times 5 = 500$

$25 \times 4 = 100$

$\underline{25}$

625

Or, accept any estimate within reason.

DAY 5

In the past, 25 cents was sometimes called "two bits." If you wanted to
refer to $1.00 in bits, how many "bits" would it be?

5

Eight bits

25 cents = 2 bits, and there are 4 groups of $0.25 in
$1.00, so $4 \times 2 = 8$ bits.

Teacher's Notes

1

FOUR and SIX

$4 + 6 = 10$ and $4 \times 6 = 24$

2

211

Since the sum of the numbers is 4, 2 is the only digit that can be used in the hundreds place. Therefore, the sum of the odd digits for the ones and tens places must be 2.

3

6:53, 3:56, 5:36

DAY 1

Use these letters to make two number words that have a sum of 10 and a product of 24.

F   I   X

O   U   R   S

DAY 2

I am a 3-digit number.
My hundreds digit is an even number.
My tens digit and my ones digit are odd numbers.
The sum of my digits is 4.

What number am I?

DAY 3

A digital clock shows 6:35.

What other times could a digital clock show using these same numbers?

DAY 4

Mr. Lang has two white shirts, one blue shirt, and one plaid shirt.

1. What percent of all of the shirts are white?

2. What percent of all of the shirts are plaid?

4

1. 50%

2. 25%

One half of the shirts are white.
One fourth of the shirts are plaid.

DAY 5

A year has 365 days, except in a leap year when there are 366 days.
A leap year occurs every four years. Is it possible to have 3 leap years
in a 10-year period?

5

Yes

The 1st, 5th, and 9th years or the 2nd, 6th, and 10th
years would be leap years.

Teacher's Notes

1

42

The only other multiple of 7 between 40 and 50 is 49, which is an odd number.

2

1. Brett; 1 square meter

2. Brett's room is a square and Elaine's is a rectangle.

A diagram of the two rooms described in the problem may help the visual learner.

3

Paul was born in 1979 and Pam was born in 1988.

DAY 1

What even 2-digit number between 40 and 50 is a multiple of 7?

DAY 2

Elaine's room is 6 meters long and 4 meters wide. Brett's room is 5 meters long and 5 meters wide.

1. Whose room has the greater area and by how much?

2. What shapes are their rooms?

DAY 3

Mia was born in 1983. Her brother Paul was born four years before Mia, and her sister Pam was born nine years after Paul.

In what years were Paul and Pam born?

DAY 4

Copy the figures. Draw one line through each figure to change it into two different figures.

1.

2.

3.

4

Answers may vary. Possible answers:

1. Change into 2 triangles
2. Change into 2 squares
3. Change into a square and a rectangle

1. **2.** **3.**

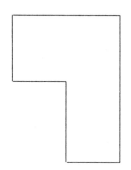

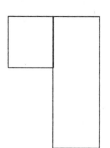

DAY 5

The area of each square is 1 square centimeter.

Find the areas of the figures.

1.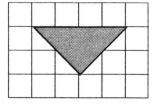

2.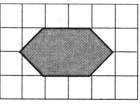

3.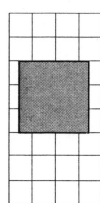

5

1. 4 square centimeters
2. 9 square centimeters
3. 6 square centimeters

1. The maple tree; The elm is 3 feet taller than the maple. The oak is 1 foot taller than the maple since it is 2 feet shorter than the elm.

2.
1. $\frac{65}{100}$
2. 0.65

3. One half dollar, one quarter, two dimes, and one nickel

DAY 1

The elm tree is 3 feet taller than the maple tree. The oak tree is 2 feet shorter than the elm tree. Which is the shortest tree? Explain.

DAY 2

At the Ocean County Fair, sixty-five out of one hundred couples entered the square-dance contest.

1. What fraction of the couples entered the square-dance contest?

2. Write this number as a decimal.

DAY 3

Joanna has one dollar in coins. She has 5 different coins.

What are the 5 coins?

Daily Mathematics / Week 25

DAY 4

Make the pattern. There is one dot in the first row, 2 dots in the second, 1 dot in the third, 3 dots in the fourth, 1 dot in the fifth, and 4 dots in the sixth.

How many dots do you think there will be in the twelfth row? The fifteenth row?

4

Twelfth row: 7; fifteenth row: 1

You may want to ask students to describe the pattern. There is one dot in every odd-numbered row. There are 2 dots in the first even-numbered row. Then the number of dots in the even-numbered rows continues to increase by 1.

DAY 5

What is the least number of hits needed to score exactly 34 points?

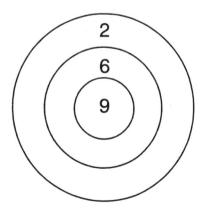

5

6 hits

$2 \times 9 = 18$, $2 \times 6 = 12$, $2 \times 2 = 4$; $18 + 12 + 4 = 34$

Encourage students to use the guess-and-check approach to solve this problem.

Teacher's Notes

1

10 ounces

2

1. 9,763

2. 2,034

3. 97,643

4. 203,467

These problems review place value and the concept of even and odd numbers.

3

West

You may suggest that students sketch a diagram of the path Jimmy and Happy walked. Or, you can put this diagram on the board to help students with directions:

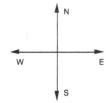

DAY 1

Vera fills an 8-ounce glass with orange juice.
She drinks 5 ounces, then fills the glass again.
She drinks more of the orange juice, and now has 3 ounces left.

How many ounces did Vera drink?

DAY 2

Use these numbers.   9   3   7   4   6   0   2

1. Write the greatest 4-digit odd number.

2. Write the least 4-digit even number.

3. Write the greatest 5-digit number.

4. Write the least 6-digit number.

DAY 3

Jimmy took his dog, Happy, for a walk. They walked 2 blocks north, turned right and walked 3 blocks, turned left and walked 2 blocks, and turned left again and walked 1 block.

In what direction are Jimmy and Happy now walking?

Daily Mathematics / Week 26

DAY 4

The numbers 1, 4, and 9 are called *square numbers.*

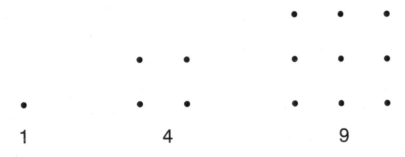

1   4   9

What are the next three square numbers?

16, 25, 36

Suggest that students extend the diagram patterns. Continue to add a row and a column to each square. Each row and each column will have one more dot than the rows and the columns of the previous square.

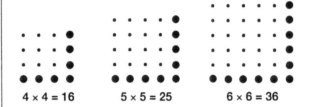

$4 \times 4 = 16$ $5 \times 5 = 25$ $6 \times 6 = 36$

You can extend the problem by asking students to find the 10th square number. (100)

DAY 5

1. How many sweaters in size small are in stock?

2. How many more size medium sweaters than size large sweaters does the store have in stock?

3. What is the total number of sweaters the store has in stock?

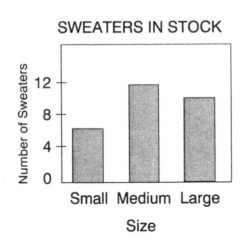

SWEATERS IN STOCK

Number of Sweaters

12
8
4
0

Small   Medium   Large

Size

5

1. 6 sweaters   **2.** 2 more   **3.** 28 sweaters

Students may need help reading this graph because the vertical axis is labeled in increments of 4. You may need to point out that there are 6 size small sweaters and 10 size large. Six is the even number between 4 and 8, and 10 is the even number between 8 and 12 on the vertical axis.

Teacher's Notes

1

José: 6th; Kitty: 3rd; Matt: 1st

Since the top floor is the sixth floor, José lives on the sixth, Kitty lives on 6 – 3, or the third floor, and Matt lives on 3 – 2, or the first floor.

2

No; Mr. Li only has 9 yards of string because 27 ÷ 3 = 9. Students may need to be reminded that there are 3 feet in a yard.

3

1. 89,000

2. The tens digit, the hundreds digit, and the thousands digit

This problem reviews place value.

DAY 1

In a 6-story building, Matt lives 2 floors below Kitty. José lives on the top floor which is 3 floors above Kitty. What floor do each of them live on?

DAY 2

Mr. Li wants to wrap a box that is 10 yards around. He has 27 feet of string. Can he wrap the box? Explain your answer.

DAY 3

1. What number is 120 greater than 88,880?

2. In what places did the digits change?

In the problem, the letters stand for numbers.

1. If *A* is 1 and *B* is 2, what is *C*?

2. If *B* is 6 and *C* is 16, what is *A*?

3. If *C* is 9, what is *A* + *B*?

$$
\begin{array}{r}
A \\
3 \\
+\ B \\
\hline
C
\end{array}
$$

4

1. $C = 6$

2. $A = 7$

3. $A + B = 6$

Students should understand that they need to substitute the given values in the problems in order to solve them. They will use their knowledge of basic addition and subtraction facts to solve each problem.

The basketball team scored 63 points in the first game, 12 fewer points in the second game, and 54 points in the third game.

1. What is the median of the team's scores?

2. What is the range?

5

1. 54 points

2. 12 points

You may need to remind students that the median is the middle score and the range is the difference between the highest and the lowest scores.

1

6 tires

A bicycle has 2 tires, a tricycle has 3 tires, and a unicycle has 1 tire. You may want to point out that the prefix *uni* means one, the prefix *bi* means two, and the prefix *tri* means three.

DAY 1

Pete is fixing flat tires on a bicycle, a tricycle, and a unicycle.

How many flat tires is he fixing?

2

1. Cary: 35 minutes
   Larry: 70 minutes, or 1 hour 10 minutes

2. 11:40 A.M.

DAY 2

Cary and Larry went boating. Cary rowed the boat from 9:55 A.M. to 10:30 A.M. Larry rowed the boat twice as long as Cary, and started at 10:30 A.M.

1. How long did each person row the boat?

2. What time did Larry finish rowing?

3

54 divided by 6 is equal to 8 plus 1.

Encourage students to check to see if the number sentence is true. 54 ÷ 6 = 8 + 1

9 = 9

DAY 3

Make a number sentence from the following words and numbers.

plus   54   8   is equal to

6   divided by   1

Daily Mathematics / Week 28

DAY 4

Draw each figure. Then draw the line or lines that divide the figure into two equal parts.

1.

2.

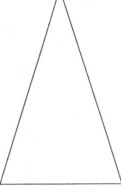

3.

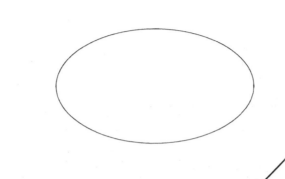

4

1. 2. 3.

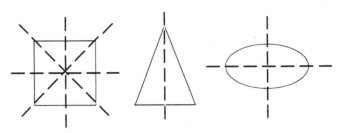

You may want to point out that a line that divides a figure into two equal figures is called a *line of symmetry*. Some figures have many lines of symmetry, some have one, and some have none. You may want to extend this problem by asking students how many lines of symmetry a circle has. (An infinite number)

DAY 5

Rearrange the 7 toothpicks to form 3 triangles.

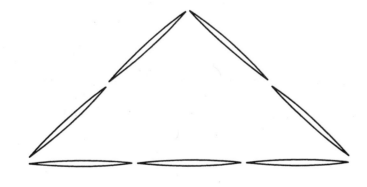

5

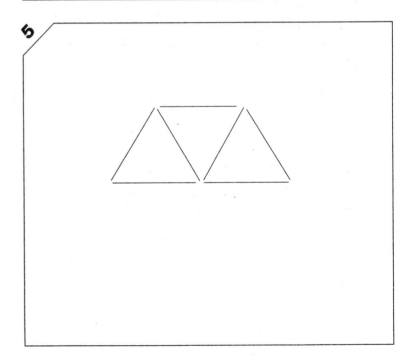

Daily Mathematics / Week 29

1

1:01, 1:11, 1:21, 1:31, 1:41, 1:51; 12:21

DAY 1

At what times does a digital clock show palindromes between 1 o'clock and 2 o'clock? Between 12 o'clock and 1 o'clock?

2

1. 20   **2.** 13   **3.** 24   **4.** 9

Remind students to always work within the parentheses first. You may want to point out that in problem 1, you add first, then multiply. But in problem 2, you multiply first, then add. The same is true in problems 3 and 4.

You may want to emphasize that the order in which operations are performed can change the value of the expression.

DAY 2

Find the answers.

1. $(7 + 3) \times 2$

2. $7 + (3 \times 2)$

3. $(15 - 3) \times 2$

4. $15 - (3 \times 2)$

3

Mac: $1\frac{1}{2}$ miles; Zeb: 2 miles; Jack: $\frac{1}{2}$ mile

You may want to suggest that students divide the number of laps each boy ran by 4.

DAY 3

Mac ran 6 laps around the track, Zeb ran 8 laps, and Jack ran 2 laps. If each lap is equal to $\frac{1}{4}$ mile, how many miles did they each run?

Daily Mathematics / Week 29

Millicent takes 35 minutes to get ready for school in the morning. It takes her 15 minutes to get to school. If Millicent has to be at school by 8:45 A.M., what time should she get up in the morning?

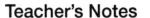

7:55 A.M.

Students can use the strategy of working backward to solve this problem. 15 + 35 = 50 minutes and 50 minutes before 8:45 is 7:55.

Find each answer. Tell which method you used: paper and pencil, a calculator, or mental math.

1.	403	2.	7,945	3.	2,002	4.	325
	+ 297		+ 4,087		− 450		− 100

Methods will vary.

1. 700; mental math

2. 12,032; paper and pencil or calculator

3. 1,552; paper and pencil

4. 225; mental math

You may want to stress that there is more than one way to solve a problem. Students will also learn when it is appropriate to use a calculator. Sometimes mental math or paper and pencil computation is quicker.

Teacher's Notes

1

1. 10 years

2. 7 years

You may want to remind students that the median age is the middle age and the range of the ages is the difference between the youngest child's age and the oldest child's age. You can extend these problems by asking students to find the mean, or average, age. ([8 + 10 + 15] ÷ 3 = 11)

2

1. 897

2. 5,987

3. 7,986

These problems review place value and practice rounding numbers.

3

1. 6 + 5 − 4 = 7

2. (6 − 4) x 8 = 16

3. 8 − 4 + 5 = 9

4. (4 + 5) x 6 = 54

DAY 1

Mr. Callas has 3 children, ages 8, 10, and 15.

1. What is the median of their ages?

2. What is the range of their ages?

DAY 2

Use these digits.   2   8   1   7

5   9   6

1. Make a 3-digit number as close as possible to 900.

2. Make a 4-digit number as close as possible to 6,000.

3. Make a 4-digit number as close as possible to 8,000.

DAY 3

To solve the problems, use $A = 6$, $B = 4$, $C = 5$, and $D = 8$.

1. $A + C - B = ?$ **2.** $(A - B) \times D = ?$

3. $D - B + C = ?$ **4.** $(B + C) \times A = ?$

DAY 4

Misha, Luke, Paul, and Heidi collect quarters, dimes, nickels, and pennies. Misha does not collect dimes. Luke collects pennies. Paul does not collect quarters. Heidi does not collect dimes or nickels.

What coins do they each collect?

Misha: nickels; Luke: pennies; Paul: dimes; Heidi: quarters

Suggest that students draw a similar table to fill in as they draw conclusions.

	Pennies	Dimes	Nickels	Quarters
Misha	no	no	yes	no
Luke	yes	no	no	no
Paul	no	yes	no	no
Heidi	no	no	no	yes

DAY 5

Mary Clare is serving ham, tuna, cheese, and turkey sandwiches at her party. She is also serving juice and milk. If each guest wants a sandwich and a drink, how many different choices do they have? What are they?

8 choices: ham sandwich and milk, ham sandwich and juice, tuna sandwich and milk, tuna sandwich and juice, cheese sandwich and milk, cheese sandwich and juice, turkey sandwich and milk, and turkey sandwich and juice

You may want to arrange this information in a tree diagram.

Teacher's Notes

1

1. K

2. 6

3.

In problem 1, the pattern begins with *A* and skips every other letter. In problem 2, the pattern contains the multiples of 6 backward from 36. In problem 3, the number of the sides of each figure increases by 1.

2

1. 8 liters   2. 15 meters

You may want to bring a gallon container, a pint container, a liter container, a milliliter container, a yardstick, a meter stick, and a 12-inch ruler to class. Seeing these objects may help the visual learner make better estimates.

3

60 years old

Karen is 12 years old. 5 x 12 = 60

DAY 1

What comes next?

1. A, C, E, G, I, _____

2. 36, 30, 24, 18, 12, _____

3. , _____

DAY 2

1. Which is closest to 2 gallons?

   8 pints   8 liters   8 milliliters

2. Which is closest to 15 yards?

   15 kilometers   15 feet   15 meters

DAY 3

Karen's grandmother is 5 times as old as Karen. Karen's mother was 20 years old when she was born, and is 32 years old now.

How old is Karen's grandmother?

DAY 4

Oklahoma — 1907   Virginia — 1788

Hawaii — 1959   Maine — 1820

Ohio — 1803   Delaware — 1787

1. Order the states by the dates that they joined the United States. Put the earliest date first.

2. In 1990, how long had each of these states been a part of the United States?

4

1. Delaware, Virginia, Ohio, Maine, Oklahoma, and Hawaii

2. Oklahoma: 83 years; Hawaii: 31 years; Ohio: 187 years; Virginia: 202 years; Maine: 170 years; Delaware: 203 years

DAY 5

You have a bag that contains 12 red marbles, 7 blue marbles, and 3 yellow marbles. If you choose one marble from the bag without looking, what color marble do you think you will pick? Explain.

5

Red; Because there are more red marbles than blue or yellow marbles, you have a greater chance of pulling a red marble out of the bag.

Teacher's Notes

1

Cube

Suggest that students draw a sketch of the figure from the description. Then, encourage them to create their own space-figure riddles for other students to solve.

2

Helia; 40 minutes

Darryl studied for $2\frac{1}{3}$ hours, or 140 minutes.
Helia studied for 180 minutes, or 3 hours.

3

10 pounds

Students can solve this problem by using the guess-and-check method.

DAY 1

I am a space figure. I have 6 flat faces, 12 straight edges, and 8 corners. What figure am I?

DAY 2

Darryl spent $2\frac{1}{3}$ hours studying for his history test. Helia spent 180 minutes studying for the test. Who studied longer, and by how much?

DAY 3

Teri's dog and cat weigh 28 pounds together. Her dog weighs 8 pounds more than her cat. How much does Teri's cat weigh?

Daily Mathematics / Week 32

DAY 4

Match.

Column 1		Column 2	
1.	$\dfrac{4}{100}$	a.	0.04
2.	$\dfrac{50}{100}$	b.	0.4
3.	$\dfrac{4}{10}$	c.	0.05
4.	$\dfrac{5}{100}$	d.	0.50

4

1. a   2. d   3. b   4. c

DAY 5

The Roxford Express Train has 10 cars. One is the locomotive and one is for cargo. Four of the cars seat 50 passengers and the rest seat 48. How many passengers can be seated on the train?

5

392 passengers

There are 8 cars that seat passengers:
$4 \times 50 = 200$, $4 \times 48 = 192$, $200 + 192 = 392$

Daily Mathematics / Week 33

DAY 1

Arrange these numbers in order, from least to greatest.

three tenths   0.08 $\dfrac{7}{10}$

0.08, $\dfrac{7}{10}$, three tenths

Suggest that students express all the numbers as fractions or decimals.

0.08 = $\dfrac{8}{100}$; $\dfrac{7}{10}$ = 0.7; and $\dfrac{3}{10}$ = 0.3

DAY 2

Billy has four cards numbered 5, 7, 4, and 8. He picks one card. The card contains the only number that 80 is not divisible by. Which card did he pick?

The card that contains 7.

You may want to point out that 5, 4, and 8 are all factors of 80.

DAY 3

Rick needs 40 hot dog buns for the party. The buns are sold in packages of 6. How many packages should Rick buy?

---

7 packages

Since the hot dog buns are sold in packages of 6, Rick will need to buy more buns than he needs. You can extend this question by asking students how many buns will be left over. (2)

DAY 4

Find the 2-digit number whose digits add up to 11 and multiply out to 30.

56

Suggest that students use the guess-and-check approach to solve this problem. A table would help them organize their thinking.

Addends of 11	Product of addends	
1 + 10 = 11	1 × 10 = 10	no
2 + 9 = 11	2 × 9 = 18	no
3 + 8 = 11	3 × 8 = 24	no
4 + 7 = 11	4 × 7 = 28	no
5 + 6 = 11	5 × 6 = 30	yes

DAY 5

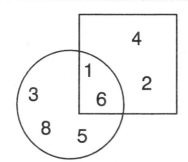

1. What is the sum of the numbers in the square but not in the circle?

2. What is the sum of the numbers in the square and the circle?

3. What is the sum of the numbers not in the square?

4. What is the sum of the numbers in the circle or the square?

5

1. 6   **2.** 7   **3.** 16   **4.** 29

These questions preview the concepts of union and intersection of sets. The word *and* implies intersection, or numbers common to both the circle and the square. The word *or* implies union, or all numbers in the square or circle together.

DAY 1

Seven men married seven women. Each couple had 4 children.

How many children are there?

1

28 children

The 7 men and 7 women are 7 couples: 7 × 4 = 28.

Some students may not read the problem carefully and multiply 7 × 7 × 4.

DAY 2

Mr. Carter drives 25 miles each way to work. He works a six-day week. Mrs. Carter drives 40 miles round trip to work. She works a five-day week.

Who drives the greater number of miles in a work week?

2

Mr. Carter

He drives 25 miles each way, or 50 miles per day × 6 days = 300 miles; Mrs. Carter drives 40 miles per day × 5 days = 200 miles.

DAY 3

Doug made 9 posters for the school play and Alice made 6 posters. They hung $\frac{1}{3}$ of the posters in the cafeteria. How many posters did they hang in the cafeteria?

3

5 posters

Students may solve this problem by finding $\frac{1}{3}$ of 9 and $\frac{1}{3}$ of 6, or $\frac{1}{3}$ of 15.

Daily Mathematics / Week 34

 DAY 4

Which of the figures can be flipped to fit on top of each other?

A

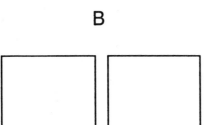

B

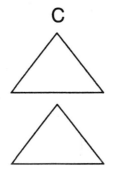

C

4

Figures A and B

This problem previews the concept of reflections.

 DAY 5

Which of the figures are congruent?

A

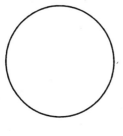

B

C

5

Figure B

Congruent figures have the same shape and the same size. Figures A and C are similar — they have the same shape, but not the same size. All congruent figures are similar, but not all similar figures are congruent.

1

8 washing machines

They can only wash 63 pounds in 7 machines.

DAY 1

The Clean-U Laundry Company has 66 pounds of shirts to wash. Each of the washing machines holds 9 pounds of wash. How many machines do they need to wash all of the shirts?

2

104 feet

$7 \times 4 = 28$, $6 \times 4 = 24$, $8 \times 4 = 32$, and $10 \times 2 = 20$;
$28 + 24 + 32 + 20 = 104$

DAY 2

Seven antelope, six elands, eight deer, and ten cranes were all in the water. How many feet were in the water?

3

Sean

Sean traveled $600 \div 5$, or 120, miles per day.
Belinda traveled $800 \div 8$, or 100, miles per day.

DAY 3

Sean traveled 600 miles in 5 days. Belinda traveled 200 miles farther than Sean in 8 days. Who traveled farther per day?

Daily Mathematics / Week 35

DAY 4

Complete the puzzle.

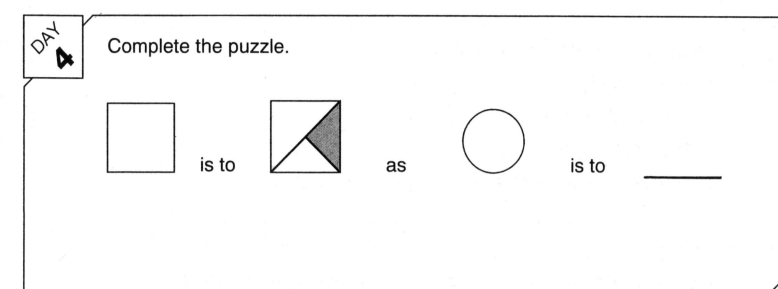

is to [triangle figure] as [circle figure] is to _____

4

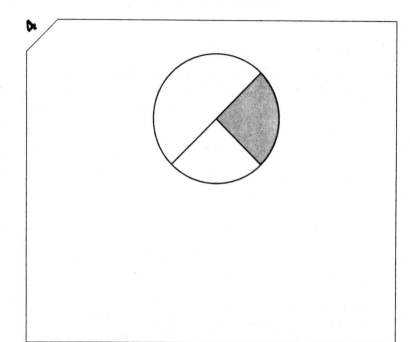

DAY 5

Each side of the cube is painted. No two sides that are next to each other are the same color. Only three colors are used. What colors are the sides you cannot see?

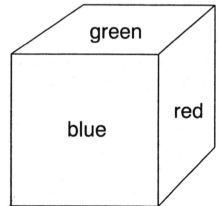

5

Left side: red; back side: blue; base: green

Opposite sides will have the same color. You may want to bring in a cube to help the visual learner answer the question.

1

Estimates will vary.

Provide students with a centimeter ruler or a meter stick so that they can check their estimates.

Estimate each distance in centimeters.

1. Your height

2. The length of your foot

3. The width of your hand

4. The distance from the tip of your pinkie to your elbow

2

8 students

This is a tricky problem. Students might answer 24 children. They should be encouraged to read the problem very carefully. The words *All but* are the key words to finding the correct answer.

There are 32 students in the class. All but 8 went outside for recess. How many students stayed inside during recess?

3

Students can respond a black marble or a white marble.

A discussion of equally likely outcomes might result. You might ask students to place a black marble and a white marble in a paper bag and pick one out without looking 50 times. They should record the result of each pick. They should then compare and discuss their results.

You place a white marble and a black marble in a paper bag and then pick one marble without looking. What color marble could you pick?

Daily Mathematics / Week 36

DAY 4

A block of wood is cut as shown. How many small squares are there in all?

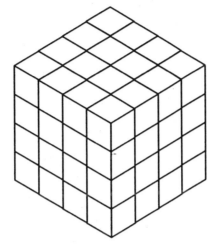

4

64 small squares

Be sure students do not forget to count the small squares that are inside the block and are not visible in the drawing. Encourage students to explain how they found the answer. There are 16 small cubes (4 × 4) on the front face of the large cube. The large cube is 4 cubes deep. Therefore, (4 × 4) × 4 = 64 small cubes.

DAY 5

1. Draw a picture to show what $\frac{1}{3}$ means.

2. Draw a picture to show what $\frac{3}{5}$ means.

3. Draw a picture to show what $\frac{3}{4}$ means.

4. Draw a picture to show what $\frac{7}{10}$ means.

5

1.- 4. Drawings will vary.

Possible answers:

1. 2.

3. 4.